THIS BOOK BELONGS TO

Colby Green
name

from Aunt Jean, Robbie & Al

EXTINCT FOR 65 MILLION YEARS, THEY'RE BACK!

Jurassic Park is a totally unique "zoo" located on Nublar Island, about 125 miles (200 km) off the coast of Costa Rica, in Central America. The fulfillment of five years work, is a dream come true for John Hammond, a businessman who made his fortune creating theme parks and zoos around the world.

Imagine an island covered with lush vegetation and inhabited by . . .
LIVE DINOSAURS!

HOW JURASSIC PARK BEGAN

First, paleontologists discovered dinosaur-age fossil mosquitoes (blood-sucking insects) preserved in chunks of amber. The insects' stomachs still contained the preserved blood of dinosaurs they bit more than 65 million years ago. Genetic scientists were then able to remove the ancient dinosaur DNA (the genetic code that acts as a blueprint for creating life) and, with the help of powerful computers, they created living dinosaur embryos.

Dinosaurs are a group of ancient reptiles that lived on the Earth long before human beings appeared. No one had ever seen a living dinosaur before . . . until now!

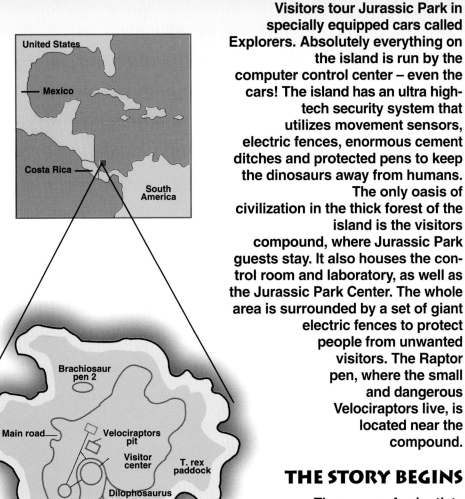

United States

Mexico

Costa Rica

South America

Brachiosaur pen 2

Main road

Velociraptors pit

Visitor center

T. rex paddock

Dilophosaurus pen

Dock

Vista view

Access road

Helipad

Brachiosaur pen 1

Visitors tour Jurassic Park in specially equipped cars called Explorers. Absolutely everything on the island is run by the computer control center – even the cars! The island has an ultra high-tech security system that utilizes movement sensors, electric fences, enormous cement ditches and protected pens to keep the dinosaurs away from humans.
The only oasis of civilization in the thick forest of the island is the visitors compound, where Jurassic Park guests stay. It also houses the control room and laboratory, as well as the Jurassic Park Center. The whole area is surrounded by a set of giant electric fences to protect people from unwanted visitors. The Raptor pen, where the small and dangerous Velociraptors live, is located near the compound.

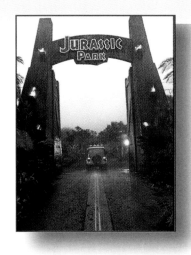

THE STORY BEGINS

The group of scientists and visitors arriving at Jurassic Park are about to be the first to tour the park and see living dinosaurs, before the official opening.

The weather is beautiful now, but a tropical storm is heading for the island at lightning speed.

Everything seems fine, but things are about to go very wrong . . .

HERE ARE THE EIGHT CHARACTERS WHO WILL EXPLORE JURASSIC PARK WITH YOU

DR. ELLIE SATTLER

Dr. Ellie Sattler is a paleobotanist, a scientist who studies fossil plants. She's come to Jurassic Park to assist Dr. Grant with the inspection.

TIM

Tim is the nine-year-old grandson of John Hammond. A big dinosaur buff, he's on the island to visit his grandpa — and Dr. Grant, his hero.

DR. ALAN GRANT

Dr. Alan Grant, a paleontologist who studies the skeletons and behavior of carnivorous dinosaurs, has been invited to Jurassic Park to inspect the facilities before the official park opening.

JOHN HAMMOND

John Hammond is a billionaire business-man who accomplished his dream to build Jurassic Park. Totally obsessed by dinosaurs, he has invented a new kind of theme park. His company, InGen Corporation, created Jurassic Park and all its dinosaurs.

DR. IAN MALCOLM

Dr. Ian Malcolm is a mathematical genius here to inspect the operations. However, he doesn't believe that science can always control complex natural systems. He's certain that something will eventually go wrong with the park.

DENNIS NEDRY

Dennis Nedry programmed all the computer systems in Jurassic Park. He secretly decided to sell frozen dinosaur embryos to a rival company for a lot of money. To sneak the embryos off the island, he uses the computer to turn off the Jurassic Park security system. Unfortunately, his program eventually shuts down all island control systems. Now none of the electric fences are operational and the dinosaurs will soon discover that they can escape!

ALEXIS (LEX)

Lex is Tim's 12-year-old sister. She's as crazy about computers as Tim is about dinosaurs, and she has a crush on Dr. Grant.

ROBERT MULDOON

Robert Muldoon is the island game warden. Although he's worked with dangerous wild animals for years, he doesn't trust the dinosaurs — especially the Velociraptors.

NOW, IT'S TIME TO MEET ONE OF THE INHABITANTS OF JURASSIC PARK . . .

DILOPHOSAURUS

Meaning of name:
Two-Ridged Reptile

Carnivorous, Saurischian Dinosaur

Lived: 210 million years ago

Family Ceratosauridae

Found in North America.

First discovered in 1942,
Kayenta Formation, Arizona, USA

Scientifically described by Dr. Samuel Welles as a new
species of Megalosaurus, in 1954

Renamed Dilophosaurus in 1970 after the discovery of
several new and more complete fossil skeletons

Maximum known body size:
20 feet / 6 meters long, 10 feet / 3 meters tall

Skull length:
1 foot 6 inches / 0.5 meter

Weight:
1,000 pounds / 0.5 metric tonne

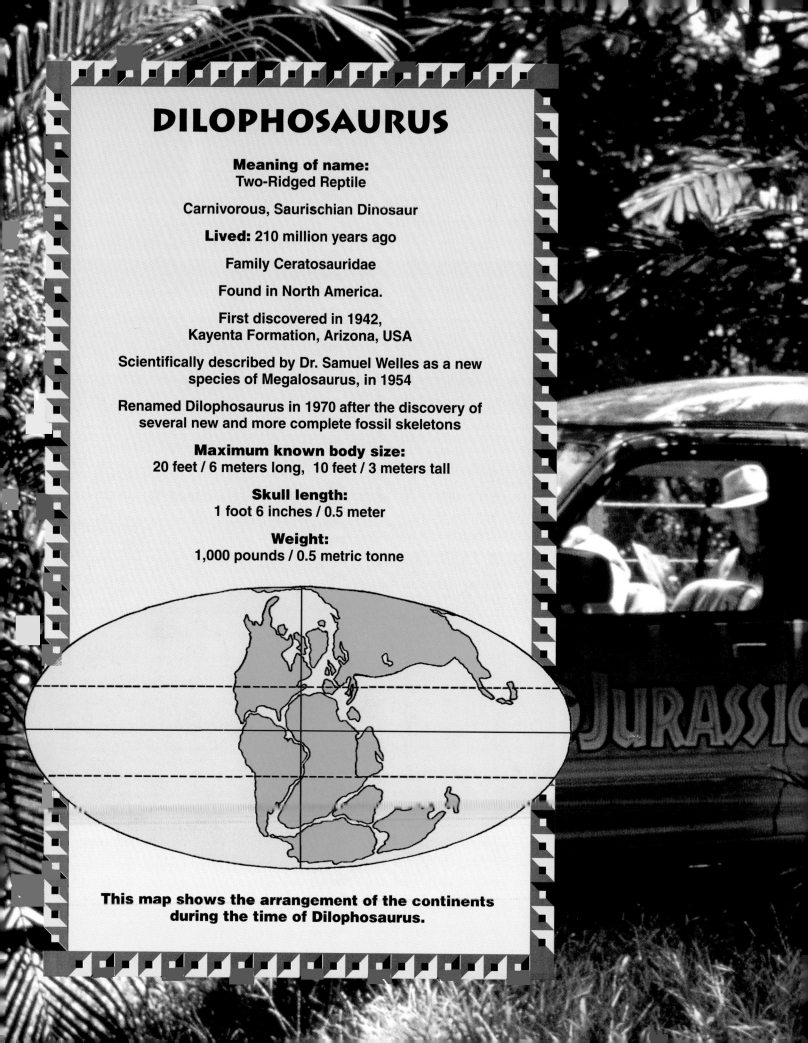

**This map shows the arrangement of the continents
during the time of Dilophosaurus.**

Visitors tour Jurassic Park in computer-controlled Explorer vehicles. They are driven through the park and stop at different pens to observe each type of dinosaur in natural environments. The first area visitors come to is the Dilophosaurus pen. This creature is active mostly at night, so it is seldom seen during daylight hours. Dilophosaurus is described as a curious animal that is rarely aggressive, despite its tremendous mouthful of teeth and poisonous venom. It gets around by hopping, much like a kangaroo.

DILOPHOSAURUS

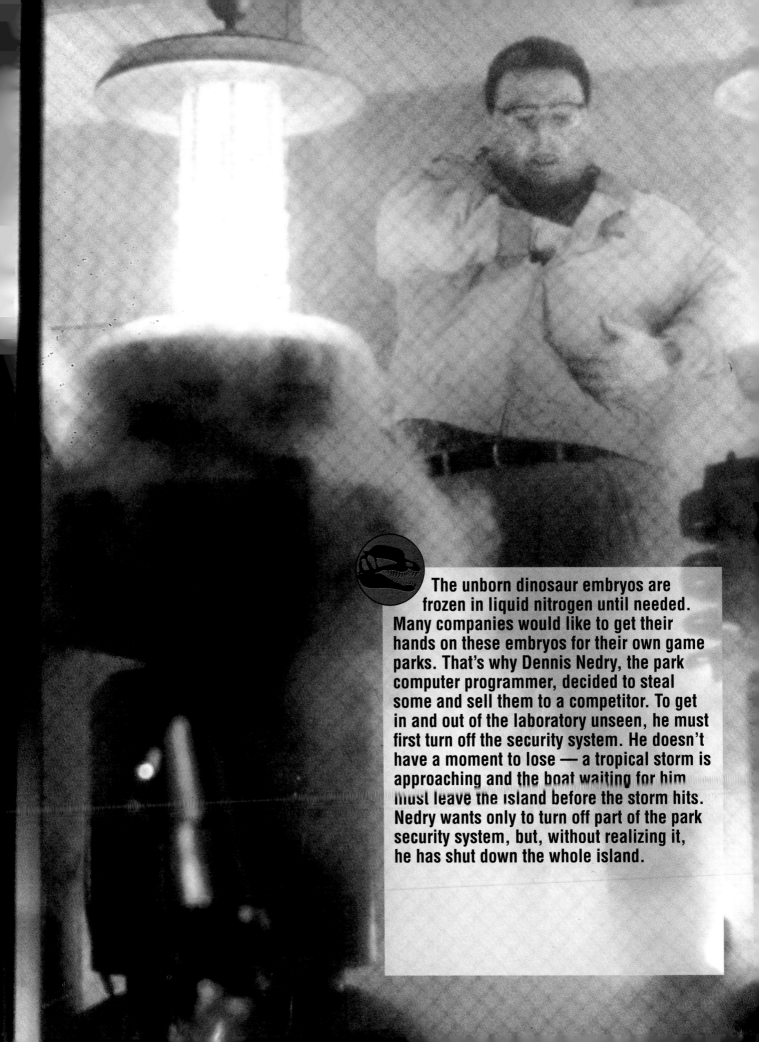

The unborn dinosaur embryos are frozen in liquid nitrogen until needed. Many companies would like to get their hands on these embryos for their own game parks. That's why Dennis Nedry, the park computer programmer, decided to steal some and sell them to a competitor. To get in and out of the laboratory unseen, he must first turn off the security system. He doesn't have a moment to lose — a tropical storm is approaching and the boat waiting for him must leave the island before the storm hits. Nedry wants only to turn off part of the park security system, but, without realizing it, he has shut down the whole island.

Dilophosaurus was one of the first large meat-eating dinosaurs.
In fact, it is the best preserved large dinosaur from the early Jurrasic period.
Like Tyrannosaurus, there are two different forms of Dilophosaurus, one larger and
more bulky, the other almost as large, but very slightly built. Perhaps, as with
Tyrannosaurus, these differences represent male and female animals.

The size of an adult Dilophosaurus compared to a six-foot (1.85 m) human.

Stuffing the stolen embryos in his coat pocket, he jumps in a jeep and leaves the Park Center. The storm has hit and the rain makes driving difficult. Nedry can't see where he is going and takes a wrong turn. The jeep skids and plows into the mud. Nedry decides to use the cable winch on the jeep to pull it back onto the road. Suddenly, he hears a clear but strange hoot from the forest. He turns around and sees the head of Dilophosaurus sticking out from behind a tree.

Although Dilophosaurus fossils are currently found in only one small area of Arizona in the United States, Dilophosaurus likely lived throughout North America. Other deposits of rocks of the Dilophosaurus age are found on the east coast of the United States and Canada. Most of the fossils found in the other locations are dinosaur footprints that show many Dilophosaurus-sized dinosaurs lived there. Unfortunately, it seems that areas that preserve dinosaur footprints well are not always the best areas to preserve bones. So for now, the only place where Dilophosaurus fossils are truly known is Arizona.

This map shows where bones of Dilophosaurus have been found.

The Dilophosaurus springs out from behind the tree. Despite its threatening appearance, it seems curious and even friendly. Slowly, the dinosaur approaches Nedry and then follows him, step for step. In a hurry to deliver the frozen embryos and frustrated at being stuck in the mud, Nedry gets impatient with the animal.

There were more than 60 sharp teeth in the mouth of Dilophosaurus. Unlike the thick banana-shaped teeth of Tyrannosaurus, these were long knife-like blades, used both to hold and to pull apart its prey.

The front and back edges of most meat-eating dinosaur teeth had small, sharp ridges called serrations that helped the teeth cut meat more efficiently. The serrations on Dilophosaurus teeth are very small and close together.

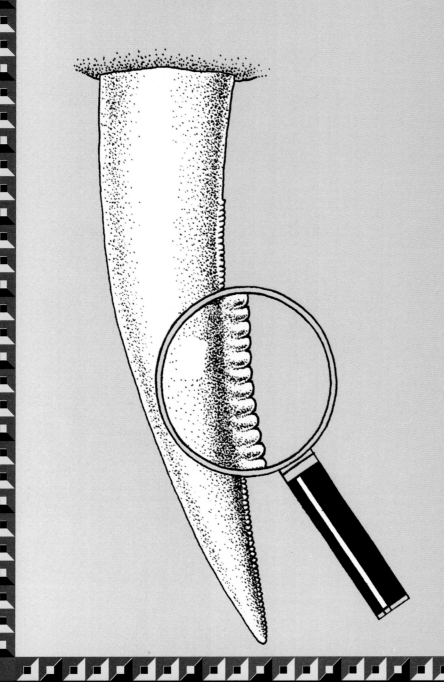

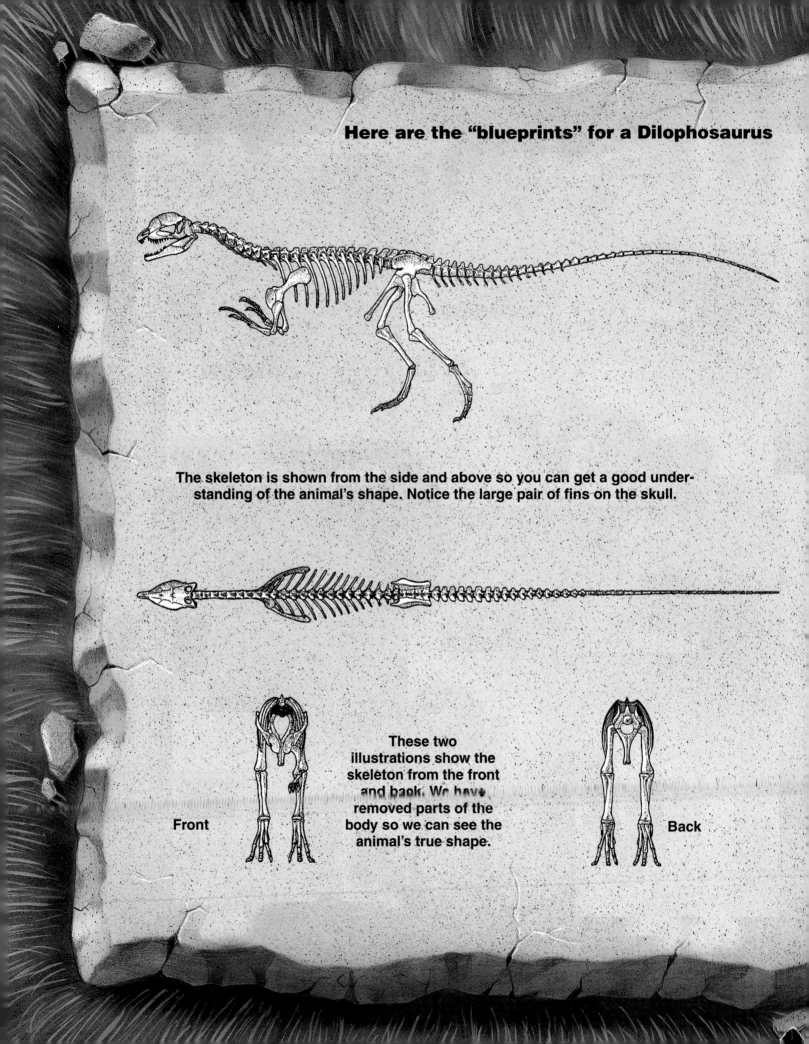

Here are the "blueprints" for a Dilophosaurus

The skeleton is shown from the side and above so you can get a good under-standing of the animal's shape. Notice the large pair of fins on the skull.

These two illustrations show the skeleton from the front and back. We have removed parts of the body so we can see the animal's true shape.

Front

Back

and the muscles that cover its bones.

The powerful muscles of Dilophosaurus allowed it to both
hold up its weight and be a fast-moving hunter. Every animal with a
backbone uses its hard skeleton to anchor the muscles.
Scientists can reconstruct the appearance of dinosaurs by
examining fossil bones for the marks left by the muscle
attachments, and by comparing them to the modern cousins of the
dinosaur — crocodiles and birds.

Now angry, Nedry throws a stick near the Dilophosaurus, hoping it will run after it and leave him to free his jeep.
The Dilophosaurus seems intrigued by this strange human creature and bizarre machine. The animal stares at Nedry and hoots again. Realizing the boat has probably left already, Nedry loses his temper and throws a rock at the Dilophosaurus. Hit, the Dilophosaurus starts hissing and moves toward Nedry.

The discovery of a meat-eating dinosaur skeleton is a rare event. Even when the dinosaurs were alive, plant-eating dinosaurs outnumbered meat-eaters by ten to one.

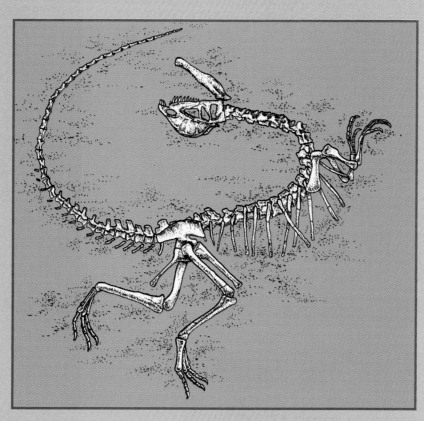

Three skeletons of Dilophosaurus were discovered by Dr. Samuel Welles in 1942. The fossil bones were very heavily encrusted in rock and it took several years of patient preparation to release them. The paired crests were not preserved in the first several specimens of Dilophosaurus. However, in 1964 Dr. Welles returned to the area where he found the original three skeletons and discovered a new and much more complete Dilophosaurus skeleton, with the skull crests preserved. Dr. Welles realized his discovery was unique among dinosaurs. Although other dinosaurs had ridges of bone on their skulls, no other meat-eating dinosaur had skull crests of this size.

The most obvious feature on the Dilophosaurus skull is the large thin pair of crests that run from behind the nostrils to the back of the skull. The crests themselves are very thin plates of bone. When a dinosaur attacks and feeds on its prey, the struggle can be very rough, even for the predator. Some scientists suggest the Dilophosaurus crests were too delicate for it to have been an active hunter. Actually, it seems likely the crests were covered with a layer of very tough skin that made them more resistant when knocked around while Dilophosaurus was attacking its prey.

Relatively little is known about the Dilophosaurus. However, it is believed it was a good hunter with a set of senses that allowed it to be a successful predator.

The angry Dilophosaurus deploys the colorful frill around its neck. The frill is a threat mechanism, to show it is not pleased! The animal opens its mouth wide, displaying numerous long and sharp teeth. Scared, Nedry backs away, forgetting the boat waiting for him at the dock. The Dilophosaurus is ready to use its best defense: like a cobra, it can spit paralyzing venom.

Nedry is sprayed with the sticky venom and falls to the ground. Slowly, he feels his arms and legs paralyze and then everything turns black.
The secret container of stolen embryos slips out of his pocket and disappears into the mud.
The Dilophosaurus is very close now. Nedry realizes his plans have failed . . .

Dilophosaurus probably fed on many types of dinosaurs and related creatures. Here is a list of some of the animals probably on its menu.

Scutellosaurus
4 feet / 1.2 meters long
Plant-eater, Armored Ornithopod Dinosaur
Bipedal (two-footed)

Massospondylus
13 feet / 4 meters long
Plant-eater, Prosauropod Dinosaur
Quadrupedal (four-footed)

Fabrosaurus
3 feet 4 inches / 1 meter long
Plant-eater, Ornithopod Dinosaur
Quadrupedal

PREHISTORIC MOBILE

You need :
Cardboard or construction paper
Markers or crayons
A coat hanger
String or fishing line

Draw dinosaur shapes on the cardboard or construction paper. Color and cut them out. Punch a hole in the head of each dinosaur.

Cut the string or fishing line in different lengths. Thread string through the holes in the dinosaurs and then hang them from the coat hanger. Tie the string in place.

For a more complicated mobile, hang more coat hangers and dinosaurs from the top coat hanger. Hang your mobile in a light breeze and watch the dinosaurs go!

Bipedal	An animal that walks on its two back legs.
Dinosaur	An extinct group of land-dwelling animals closely related to birds and reptiles.
DNA	The short name for the genetic blueprints that determine the structure of a living organism.
Embryo	A fertilized animal egg.
Fossil	Any preserved evidence of ancient life.
Ornithopod	Any of the many types of small plant-eating dinosaurs.
Paleobotanist	A scientist who specifically studies fossil plants.
Paleontologist	A scientist who studies the evidence of ancient life.
Predator	Any organism that pursues or hunts animals for food.
Prosauropod	A group of dinosaurs that gave rise to the Brontosaur family.
Quadrupedal	An animal that walks on all four legs.
Saurischian	One of the two main groups of dinosaurs; defined by the position of the bones in their hips. The bone positions resemble those of modern lizards, therefore they are called "lizard-hipped" or Saurischian.
Venom	This is form of poison usually used by predators to paralyze their prey.

Text
Lucie Duchesne and Andrew Leitch

Research
Andrew Leitch

Cover Illustration
Michel-Thomas Poulin

Illustrations
PaleoImage Ltd.

Art Direction
Studio de la Montagne
Louis C. Hébert

Desktop Publishing
Benoît Lafond and Line Godbout

Produced by
Group Potential Inc.

With photos from the movie
Jurassic Park

From a screenplay by
Michael Crichton et David Koepp

Based on a novel by
Michael Crichton